Finn And The Fair

Written by Mick Gowar
Illustrated by Tim Archbold

WAYLAND

Characters

Finn: An unfortunate Irish man

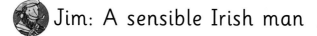

Jim: A sensible Irish man

Crook 1: A cunning fellow

Crook 2: A nasty rogue

Rich Art Collector: A very keen man

Storyteller

Storyteller: Welcome to Ballycastle. It's the day of the town fair and everyone has come to buy something or to sell something. Jim the Carter has come to buy some new strings for his banjo and to meet his best friend, Finn. Finn has come to make his fortune once again.

Jim: Hi Finn. How are you today?

 Finn: I'm grand, Jim — except I've got a dreadful headache. My mammy wants me to sell my grandfather's watch and chain and cufflinks at the fair. They're made from real gold. She said I can make a lot of money selling them.

Jim: Surely the thought of making lots of money hasn't given you a headache?

7

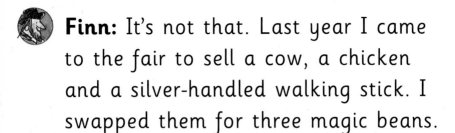

Finn: It's not that. Last year I came to the fair to sell a cow, a chicken and a silver-handled walking stick. I swapped them for three magic beans.

Jim: Did the beans grow into a magic beanstalk, with a giant's castle at the top?

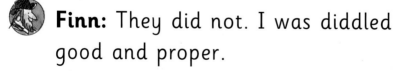 **Finn:** They did not. I was diddled good and proper.

Jim: Well, then, how did you get your headache today?

Finn: To remind me not to be so stupid this year, my mammy bopped me on the head — once for the cow, once for the chicken and once for the silver handled-walking stick. Why have you come to the fair, Jim?

Jim: I've come to buy some new strings for my banjo. Actually, I can see the banjo seller over there. You remember what your mammy told you, now, don't get diddled again!

 Finn: I mustn't get diddled again. I mustn't get diddled again. I mustn't get diddled again.

 Storyteller: But little did Finn know that this is exactly what is about to happen...

Crook 1: Will you look who it is?

 Crook 2: It's that fellow we swapped three beans for a cow, a chicken and a silver-handled stick last year.

 Crook 1: Good day, sir! And how are you today?

Finn: Not you two again! You diddled me last year. You gave me three useless beans, and I gave you a cow, a chicken and a silver-handled walking stick!

13

Crook 2: That's why we're here, Sir. To apologise.

 Finn: I don't believe you. You two are crooks and I will not get diddled again!

 Storyteller: Finn tries to walk away but the crooks chase after him.

Crook 1: Wait! Another man sold those beans to us. He told us they were magic. He was the crook, not us! We were diddled, just like you!

 Crook 2: So to make it up to you, we'd like to offer you another swap. We'll swap you a cow, a chicken and a piece of land for whatever it is you're selling at the fair today.

Storyteller: Well, that offer seems too good to refuse. A cow... a chicken... and a piece of land! Finn knows his mammy will be so proud of him for getting all these things for an old watch and chain and a pair of cufflinks!

Finn: OK, I've got a watch, a chain and a pair of cufflinks – and they're real gold!

 Crook 1: It's a deal!

 Crook 2: You won't regret your decision. Good day to you, Sir!

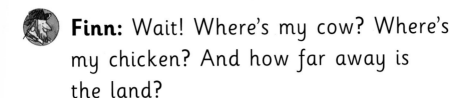 **Finn:** Wait! Where's my cow? Where's my chicken? And how far away is the land?

 **Crook 1:** Here's your land, here's your cow and, finally, here's your chicken.

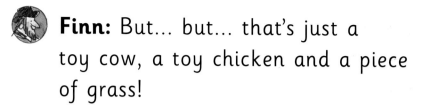 **Finn:** But... but... that's just a toy cow, a toy chicken and a piece of grass!

Crook 2: That's right. We just said a cow, a chicken and a piece of land. We never said they were real!

Finn: I've been diddled again!

Storyteller: At that moment, Jim returns carrying his banjo with brand new strings. **He** hasn't been diddled!

Jim: What have you got there, Finn?

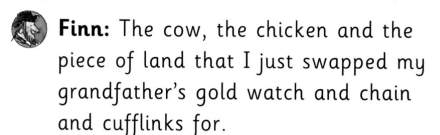 **Finn:** The cow, the chicken and the piece of land that I just swapped my grandfather's gold watch and chain and cufflinks for.

Jim: Oh, no!

Finn: Yep, I've been diddled again. Mammy is going to be **very** cross this time. What am I going to do?

21

Storyteller: Finn and Jim sit down on a bench to think about how they can get Finn out of the pickle he's in. Suddenly a rich art collector spots the land, the cow and the chicken.

Rich Art Collector: What do you call that?

 Finn: Diddled again!

 Rich Art Collector: It's fantastic! It's fabulous! It's brilliant! It's the most interesting modern sculpture I've ever seen! I must have it for my collection. Would you accept two hundred sovereigns for it?

Finn: Two hundred!

 Rich Art Collector: OK, five hundred.

 **Finn:** Five hundred!

24

Rich Art Collector: You drive a hard bargain! One thousand sovereigns, but that's my final offer. Take it or leave it!

 Jim: We'll take it. It's a fair offer, Finn.

Storyteller: Just then the two crooks return. They see the rich art collector proudly displaying his new modern sculpture.

Rich Art Collector: Look at this sculpture. Isn't it fabulous? And I only paid one thousand sovereigns for it!

Crook 1 and Crook 2: One thousand sovereigns!

Storyteller: The two crooks look at each other.

Crook 1: We've got something that's worth much more than that old sculpture. We have a watch, a chain and a pair of cufflinks, and they're all real gold!

 Rich Art Collector: I won't consider buying those!

Crook 1: Why not?

 Rich Art Collector: Well, to start with, they're not real gold!

 Crook 2: Not real gold?

29

Rich Art Collector: No. They're just painted yellow to look like gold. Do you know what's happened to you?

 Crook 1 and Crook 2: No, what?

 Rich Art Collector: You've been diddled good and proper!

START READING is a series of highly enjoyable books for beginner readers. **The books have been carefully graded to match the Book Bands widely used in schools.** This enables readers to be sure they choose books that match their own reading ability.

Look out for the Band colour on the book in our Start Reading logo.

The Bands are:

	Pink Band 1A & 1B
	Red Band 2
	Yellow Band 3
	Blue Band 4
	Green Band 5
	Orange Band 6
	Turquoise Band 7
	Purple Band 8
	Gold Band 9

START READING books can be read independently or shared with an adult. They promote the enjoyment of reading through satisfying stories supported by fun illustrations.

Mick Gowar has written more than 70 books for children, and likes to visit schools and libraries to give readings and lead workshops. He has also written plays and songs, and has worked with many orchestras. Mick writes his books in a shed in Cambridge.

Tim Archbold says that making your fortune can be a difficult thing to do. Grumpy kings are hard to please. Magic goats, golden geese and talking cats are always difficult to work with and the end of a rainbow is just over the next hill. But keep trying and remember to have some fun on the way to your fortune...